A Puppy Grows Up

by Aiden Mark
illustrated by Janice Bowles

Harcourt
SCHOOL PUBLISHERS

Printed in Mexico

ISBN 10: 0-15-350612-1
ISBN 13: 978-0-15-350612-3

Ordering Options
ISBN 10: 0-15-350598-2 (Grade 1 On-Level Collection)
ISBN 13: 978-0-15-350598-0 (Grade 1 On-Level Collection)
ISBN 10: 0-15-357758-4 (package of 5)
ISBN 13: 978-0-15-357758-1 (package of 5)

9 10   0908   15 14 13 12 11 10 09

A puppy can't clap.
It does not jog.

2

This one will grow into
this dog.

A puppy eats food
to live and grow.

Then it can dig
and jump and go!

Puppies can be red.
Or they can be black.

It can have many spots
on its back.

A puppy can't clap,
but it can run.
It can have a rest
in the sun.